Maureen Cunningham is an 87-year-old mother and grandmother from Liverpool, England. She suffers from age-related macular degeneration, which does not cause total blindness but makes everyday activities like reading and writing challenging. Maureen has always embraced new technologies, and despite being unable to see a keyboard clearly enough to type, she dictated her first book *Four Legs and a Halo,* on an iPad.

Maureen Cunningham

Illustrations by
Jan Budgen

Four Legs and a Halo

AUSTIN MACAULEY PUBLISHERS™

LONDON · CAMBRIDGE · NEW YORK · SHARJAH

Copyright © Maureen Cunningham (2019)
Illustrations by Jan Budgen

Ordering Information:
Quantity sales: special discounts are available on quantity purchases by corporations, associations, and others. For details, contact the publisher at the address below.

Publisher's Cataloging-in-Publication data

Cunningham, Maureen
Four Legs and a Halo

ISBN 9781645362753 (Paperback)
ISBN 9781645362746 (Hardback)
ISBN 9781645368700 (ePub e-book)

The main category of the book — PETS / Essays & Narratives

www.austinmacauley.com/us

First Published (2019)
Austin Macauley Publishers LLC
40 Wall Street, 28th Floor
New York, NY 10005
USA
mail-usa@austinmacauley.com
+1 (646) 5125767

To my family, my best friend Saskia, and everyone who
has ever loved a pet.

I would like to thank my niece, Jan Budgen, who illustrated this book. Jan is a retired nurse, mother, and grandmother from Liverpool. I thank her for her patience, hard work, and sense of humor.

I would also like to thank my children: Colin, Diane, Paula, and Kevin; and my grandchildren: Stephanie, Nicholas, Elizabeth, Olivia, and Amelie for encouraging me to publish this book about my pet Labrador and 'guardian' angel.

CLOSE ENCOUNTER

My name is Angel and I am a chocolate Labrador. I am ten months old and I've just had a close encounter with Death.

It all started when Mom took me to the Vet because she noticed I had a limp. I don't know what I did to get a limp but, anyway, the Vet wanted me to have tests...the usual: x-rays, blood tests—the lot. He gave Mom some pills for me. They are delicious, just like sweets.

The Vet really wasn't very nice. He asked my mom to lift me up on the table. I'm really heavy and Mom is bad with arthritis. Confidentially, she is getting on a bit. I was really mad with him.

When we went out, I was rushing to get in the car and I pulled Mom's arm and she twisted her wrist, quite bad it was. So, I had to go and stay with Diane; she is Mom's daughter. She had to look after me and it was then that IT happened.

As Diane was sorting my stuff to take back to Mom's, I noticed my yummy tablets going into the bag. Diane went upstairs to get ready and told the big fella, Paul, to keep his eye on me. Of course he didn't.

Easy peasy, I nipped up to the bag, rummaged around, and found my lovely tablets. I took them into the garden, opened the box, and got the little plastic bottle out, magic! I ate the lot and ran in the house with the bottle to show Diane how clever I was. She went absolutely mad, crying and screaming that I was going to die, phoning the Vet, Mom, Paula and giving the big fellow a piece of her mind.

Soon after that, they got me to the Vet's and he said they had to leave me there. They had to make me sick so they could count the tablets I'd taken. The next thing I knew, they gave me an injection. I was sick, sick as a dog! Now I know why they say that! Then they used a needle to put a drip into me and I couldn't stop weeing all over the place.

It was so embarrassing! I had to stay for two days.

It was awful, like being in prison.

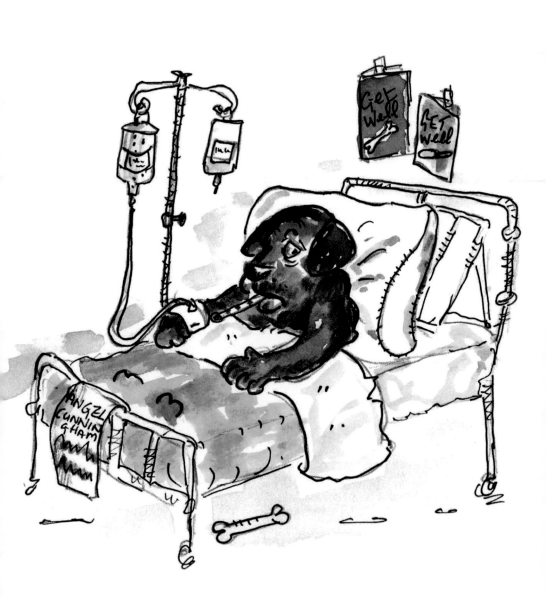

Di picked me up and took me home to Mom's.

I must say I looked as though I'd been in a War Zone. I'd got two holes in my neck and my leg had been shaved.

I wasn't a pretty sight and I could've died so I'm going to write my life story. Everyone does it these days. Everyone who thinks they are important does anyway.

Footballers do, and what do they do for a living? Only kick a ball around a field and some of them even spit!

Then there's reality stars, say no more!

So here I go...

CAR BOOT SALE

It was a bit of a struggle for food when I was little. There was a lot of pushing, shoving, and yelping and sometimes I was quite hungry. My mom was a single mom, no dad in sight to help or look after us. I think he legged it when he saw there were five of us. She managed okay. There was always a fight at meal times but we all got something.

When I was eight weeks old, I heard we were going to be SOLD. Mom was upset but she told us that we would be going to people who would love us. The next thing I knew, my brother, sisters, and me were taken in a box, put in the boot of a car, and away we went! It was dark and smelly in the boot. I didn't like it one bit and my sisters were really howling.

After a long, long time, the boot opened and three faces were peering in, oohing and aahing at us. There was a Big Face, a Midsize Face, and a Baby Face. Big Face wanted my sister but the other two wanted me. They said I was the prettiest, so off I went in luxury, in the back on Di's knee. Big Face called her that. His name was Paul and Baby Face was Elizabeth.

The next thing I remember was the car stopping at Di's mom's. Then she started oohing and aahing over me as well and we all went into her garden. I thought to myself, *This might be the start of a new life for me.* I missed my family but there was only me to eat the food here and I had my own bed.

I missed my mom but they gave me a big furry dog to play with. It didn't do much or smell like my mom. I even licked its face and cuddled in. No response at all, but it was nice and soft and I had it in my bed with me. They all thought it was funny because I was so tiny beside it. I eventually bit its nose right off. That was the end of my cuddly friend. There was all this white snowy stuff inside. I had a great time with that until Mom saw me.

PIDDLES AND PUDDLES

The family, especially Mom, used to talk about other dogs they'd had.

Danny, supposedly the wonder dog, according to Mom, never put a paw wrong. He never chewed furniture, never made a mess, never jumped up at people, and never nipped anyone, not even a little nip. The way Mom goes on, I think he should be canonized.

There was also Beau.

I think he was a bit like me. He ate his way through all the kitchen furniture, made a hole in the wall trying to escape, nearly got electrocuted as the hole was just by the electric plug and flooded the kitchen and the lounge, ruining a new carpet.

Beau also thought Danny was a wonder dog.

He thought Danny was his dad when he was little. He once put Danny in hospital. He used to swing on his neck, so much that it all swelled up. Danny looked like a hamster, I believe. I had a good laugh at that. He was too good to be true, that fellow!

Then along came Buster!

He looked like me, so they say. He was a bag of nerves when he came. I think he was a sort of rescue dog. His owners had sent him back to the kennels because they said they couldn't cope with him. The poor dog wouldn't say boo to a goose or anything else. He got better though, with TLC from all the family.

He used to go to stay with Pat and Dave, friends of the family, now and then. They loved him. It was really five star there. He slept with Dave. Poor Pat had to go in the guest room. Dave and Buster both used to snore their heads off, so Pat was glad to be in a separate room! He got the big C in the end and had to go to the Vet's. I think he's still there.

At first I couldn't make head nor tail of Mom's house. There was all this plastic sheeting all over the place. I admit, I had a few accidents here and there, and quite a lot of wees before the training started. Mom used to take me outside every half an hour and put me on the grass. After a while, I did a wee. I couldn't hold it long then. Then she'd say, "Oh, what a clever girl you are!" and I couldn't believe it, she gave me a biscuit, just for doing a wee!

Well, every time she took me outside, I obliged.

It was great! Sometimes, if I wanted a biscuit and just couldn't squeeze one out, I pretended, but she didn't twig.

The poos were a bit more difficult to keep hold of and took a bit longer. Mom was good about it though. She never shouted at me. She just sighed and picked it up in a poo bag.

She had these large white pads all over the floor. I went on them when I couldn't hold on. She said that was clever too.

I soon got the message to go outside in the garden.

THE TASTE OF MONEY

Kev came today, he's Mom's youngest.

I heard Mom say, "Put all your stuff away in the bedroom and shut the door." *Oh,* I thought, *not much I can do there.*

He carried his 'stuff' upstairs right away but he left a small bag on the settee. I was in there quick!

Not very interesting, but I got the wallet out, just to have a look. Lots of money there! I ate a couple of ten pound notes, just for starters. He came down before I could get any more.

Then he chased me! He gave me a couple of whacks on the behind. It hurt me too! He said Mom should train me better.

Poor Mom, it's always her fault! She said she'd watch for the money to come out and wash it. I chewed it first so I think it would come out in bits. I wouldn't fancy rescuing it!

SAUSAGE ROLLS

We've got two little dogs next door. They yap all the time. They don't like me. Mom calls them the Sopranos as they're always up to top doh! It was funny the other day. They had a doggy visitor. He comes sometimes because, confidentially, he can't be trusted in his house on his own. I don't know what HE could do. He's like a sausage on four stumps.

He was barking at Mom, cheeky so and so!

Mom had left the door open just a bit and I was OUT, quick as a flash. The sausage ran for his life! I chased him right down the road. His dad chased us both. He was worried what I was going to do. I just wanted to give him a fright.

He won't bark at Mom again!

I will say though, those stumps could move!

I haven't had many long walks for a while because of my sore leg. The Vet is sending me for a scan, whatever that is. I heard Mom talking on the phone and I'm going today...watch this space.

THE BONE MAN

Right, I'm home now but I've got another horror story to tell. Di and Mom both took me so I thought it must be serious. We went to this very posh place because I needed to see the 'bone' man. I didn't take to him at all. I tried very hard not to go in his room but Di had me literally by the throat; my collar and lead were pulled, and in I went.

I knew something awful was going to happen and I hid behind Mom.

He got out some pictures of legs, just legs, no bodies, and lots of bones. I was really terrified. First, he said I was going to have a scan. I didn't want anything, only to go home.

Then a nice girl came in holding a lead. I thought, *Well, she's nice.* Bone man said she would take me to the 'ward.'

I thought he meant 'walk' so I went, quite happily. I really can't remember a lot more, only it wasn't a walk at all.

THEN I WOKE UP. Someone had shaved my legs and my chest. I was bare and baldy. I don't know whether anything else had gone. I had no mirror to look at my head or my face. *OMG! WHAT AM I GOING TO DO?*

That girl came in again and put the lead on me and she took me back to that room. Mom and Di were waiting for me.

They were so pleased to see me and I was pleased to see them too. My leg was giving me 'gyp' and I just couldn't walk straight.

They got me out into the car.

I was in another world, like a foggy doggy refuge. I thought I saw the saintly Danny. He had a pair of wings and a halo, but he was saying, "It's okay now, Ange, it's all over, you'll be fine in a couple of days."

He's okay is old Dan!

Mom and Di were really fussing over me but I felt awful. My head was going round and my eyes, oh my eyes! I couldn't keep them focused at all. I just wanted to get in my own bed and stay there.

I drifted in and out. I had something to eat and felt a bit better but I couldn't be bothered being sociable. I just wanted to be left alone. I heard them laughing. I thought I was dreaming but no, I heard Mom say, "She looks like an oven ready turkey." Beautiful me!

Then Di said, "I think she looks more like Puss in Boots."

Then Paula came and that was the end! She said I was, "Just like Dick Whittington, complete with the Boots!"

That Vet had left me with bare legs and little fur socks on. I had a cropped top and bare chest. I hope Mom doesn't try to take me out for a while. All my friends will be laughing at me, especially the Sopranos next door.

Di's going to take me to Spain in a few weeks. *What will those Spanish dogs think?* And I wanted to lord it over them. I know a few bits of Spanish, I do. I can just imagine them sniggering, especially the senoritas.

THE BRA BANDIT

I have been doing a bit of thinking about when I was a puppy. I wasn't always as good as I am now. I used to have a 'thing' about bras. No, I didn't want to wear one! I just liked them.

It started when Mom was sorting the washing and a bra dropped on the floor. I picked it up for her, then it sort of twanged. It had some funny stuff at the back of it.

I was hooked! I loved to twang it!

Mom took it off me and put it with the other washing but when she wasn't looking, I got it again. *Twang, twang, twang!* Oh, I couldn't get enough of it!

From then on I used to steal them off the line when they'd been washed. Mom called me 'The Bra Napper.'

I went up to Di's house one day. Oh boy, that was a line of washing: all sorts of bras! I had a great time pulling them all off the line, *twang! twang! twang!* I was in my element, racing round the garden with one bra, then another bra, and then Diane saw me. She went mad, raving and screaming.

"They are Elizabeth's new ones! She'll kill you!"

I was a bit scared so I dropped them and ran for my life. She called me 'The Bra Snatcher,' so I had two new names. No one ever puts bras on the line anymore, I wonder why!

One thing I do not like is a mobile phone. I hate them! They frighten me, making all that noise! One day I got Mom's and ran into the garden with it, to just shut it up but it wouldn't, so I soon stopped it. I just put it in my mouth and bit it hard. Then it went into two pieces. I thought that was quite clever.

Mom now had two mobile phones!

Mom started looking for the phone soon after. She was not at all pleased with my handiwork. I got no treats for hours.

I also quite liked chewing wallpaper when nobody was in and the draft excluder was quite nice too, sort of rubbery and chewy. So after that, when they all went out as a family, I got locked in the kitchen until I learned how to behave in the house, if you please.

I had to go back to the dreaded Vet again to have my stitches out. Paula had to drag me there this time. I knew the place and that awful man, the very first one. He was still as horrible and wouldn't help Paula at all. He wouldn't even answer her questions properly.

PARTY POOPER

Kev asked Mom if she would give a little party for his children Amelie and Olivia. They were coming down to see us after their birthday. Mom agreed and they invited some of their little friends that lived in Liverpool. They live near Leeds.

They were all having hijinks and sitting around the table. I was under the table, of course, waiting for them to drop things, which they did. Yum, I was on it.

Later on, it was time to play games. They sang Happy Birthday, lit little candles on the cake, and had a few more goodies. Then Mom started to cut the cake for the ones who were going home to take with them. They all went to the door to say goodbye and left the cake just at the end of the table.

Well, I took a peep at it. It looked lovely, all pink and white with little faces on the top. I think it was a picture of the two children. I thought I'd just have a little lick of their faces. I didn't expect it to be so soft and so yummy. The next thing I knew, although I didn't really mean it, was that my face was right in the middle of the cake. In fact, it was entirely covered in cake, while they were all saying goodbye.

When they came back in, well, it was just chaos.

I was only having a taste of the cake, for goodness' sake! Kids were crying. Kev was trying to get me. I got out of there double quick, sat out of sight, licked my face clean, and then just got my head down. I knew I would never see that lovely cake again.

I heard Mom bang the lid of the dustbin down hard. I just kept a low profile until everyone had gone home, then went in and had a quiet drink; water, of course.

One night the family decided to have a barbecue and I stole a chicken joint. Paul had just put it on the window ledge to cool a little bit. I wasn't supposed to eat chicken bones but I ran off with the chicken, chased by the whole family. It was a big garden and they couldn't catch me. However, I didn't have time to really enjoy the chicken. I was eating it on the run and swallowing big chunks when I really wanted to savor it. So, once again, I was in disgrace.

Never mind, I think they called it 'being in the doghouse.'

GREEN PAWS

I had a day in the garden yesterday, with Mom. It was a really lovely day and we were out all day. Mom was cutting down bushes and I helped. I'm good at 'pruning.'

She doesn't always appreciate what I do and sometimes she gets so mad. I'm only trying to HELP!

I'm really best at digging. She digs, I dig. We have got some really nice deep holes in the garden now, all over the lawn.

I think they look quite decorative. Art can be anything these days. I haven't put anything in them yet, but I may try a few old bones. They should look quite 'arty.'

I'm also a dab hand at 'Dead Heading.' Again, I get into trouble. All flowers look the same to me. How do I know whether they're dead or alive? I got told off for that as well.

Sometimes, there's no living with Mom.

I heard her say that she's going to fill the garden with roses. I don't like roses, too prickly! I think I know why she's going to do it. I'll still find a way to get on those flowerbeds.

I'll work something out, a tunnel maybe?

WALLACE AND GROMMIT

One day we had a visit from one of Mom's friends. His name was Father Bill. He pops in now and again, but this time he had two little dogs with him. I thought they were quite cute. They had long ears and great big eyes. They gave me the once over. I remembered my manners and invited them in.

I wanted to show them round the house and garden but they wanted to stay close to their dad. I don't know whether they liked me or not, I couldn't tell.

I got my toys out. I thought we might have a game of ball in the garden but no, they didn't want to play. Mom made a cup of tea and they livened up. I think they thought there might be some food about, a bit like me! They loved their food. They were nice little fellows but not really my type. I don't think they were the outdoor sort, muddy pools etc. Those big ears would have weighed them down if they got wet.

I've never been to their house. No parties or anything. Mom apparently taught both their uncles to do 'roly-polys,' whatever they may be! Doesn't sound very interesting to me!

Oh, I've just found out those two are King Charles' spaniels! Perhaps they were not used to us mere commoners!

Mmm...

WALKIES

Mom takes me for walks along the embankment; I meet all my friends up there. Mom walks with Val and, boy, do they talk!

They never stop! Mom always has a few biscuits in her pocket and poo bags.

We usually meet poor old Millie. She's not well. She's sixteen years old and she's got the Big C. She doesn't eat much according to Vicky, her mom, but my mom gives her some of my biscuits and she will eat one or two. I don't mind a bit.

It's great up there on the embankment. No noisy cars, plenty of dogs, and nice doggy people. There are a few bikes though.

They are just a menace to us dogs. Some don't slow down at all and then complain WE are in THEIR way!

THEY are in our way! Mom usually shouts, "BIKE!" in a loud voice and I try to keep still. I used to chase them when I was small but I'm trained now. I know these things.

Sometimes we meet Thelma. She has three little dogs. They are like fluffy balls, all puffed out. They like me a lot. Thelma thinks I'm great. She says I'm well trained for my age. She keeps her girls on leads. They never get to run in the mud or anything nice like that. I think they're posh.

Sometimes we meet 'His Majesty.' He's a Red Setter and he thinks he's a cut above everyone. He just stands there waiting to be admired. Mom usually bows and says, "Good Morning, Majesty." He likes that. He's okay but hasn't got much of a sense of humor. He doesn't want to play with me.

I waited hours and hours for my walk today, Paula and Steve had a bit of a lie in. I was a bit annoyed with them.

I decided to go where 'I' wanted to go. They wanted me to go to the park. I wanted to play ball on the field.

I WON! Ha! Ha! Serves them right for being late! Twelve o'clock indeed! What time is that for a morning walk?

When Mom could drive, she used to take me to the posh park. I loved it as I used to meet all my friends and there was a lovely lady who I really got on great with. I went on holiday a couple of times to her house. Her name was Shirley. She was like the dog whisperer.

When I saw her, I used to leave Mom and trail along with her. She always had a few dogs with her. She loved me, well, everyone does. I'm a bit of a celebrity in the posh park. It must be my name.

Mom called me Angel because Diane and Paul bought me after Ken died. Ken was Mom's husband. They were married for forty-nine years and eleven and a half months. He died just before their Golden Wedding Day. Mom was very angry with God that day. I don't know God but I think he must be very powerful because Mom blamed him for Ken dying just before their Golden Wedding. Mom did apologize to the priest, Father Bill. He said God would understand. I certainly hope so.

So, I became Mom's guardian angel.

That's what she said I was and that's what I always try to be. I am also a very good housedog; that means I bark my head off if anyone comes to the door. If I don't know the person, I put on my ferocious face and growl. I wouldn't harm a fly really but they don't know that! If they are friends or okay people, Mom puts me behind her and opens the door and then I'm alright because I know she's alright.

While on the subject of Mom, I like to see that she goes to bed at a reasonable time. I think 10:30 p.m. is okay for her. She needs her sleep. What I do is this...I walk into the living room and just stand in front of her, it's always around 10:30 p.m. I don't need to look at the clock, I just know these things.

She says, "Oh, it's my bedtime, is it? Okay, I am tired so I'm going up to bed, Col."

We see her safely up the stairs, then...

Ha, ha! I jump on the settee in her place!

Col and I watch telly for a bit if there is anything decent on and then we go to bed. I always stay awake until I know everyone is fast asleep. I'm such a good guard dog.

Col lives with us now. He's Mom's son and he takes me out whenever he's off work. He works really strange hours but I think I've got my head around it now and I go to the door to wait for him.

I like chewing his slippers. I think I've probably gone through about three pairs. He says I always eat left foot slippers so he always has to buy a new pair. I don't know the difference between left and right. How does he expect me to know that?

He always takes me on nice walks. Well, I take him really! I like to go and see Cleo on my way, just to say hello. She's older than me and she can't really get out much now.

She has really bad legs. Sometimes, I believe she goes out in a pram. I've never seen it but her mom told my mom about it. Poor Cleo!

HOLIDAYS

I love the word 'Holidays.'

My first holiday was to Spain. We went by car. I love the car. I just sleep all the time. The only problem was when Di and Paul stopped for a sleep, I was raring to go. They were not amused. They usually gave me a walk and something to eat and drink so that was good. I did try my best to be good for them though, and they appreciated me. They think I'm wonderful, well I am!

Paul drove all the way to Spain but he got confused in France and we drove round and round in circles in Paris. He got completely lost. I didn't really mind because I do like a bit of culture. I saw the Trifle Tower and the Chops Elyseé. They mentioned Archy Triumph, but I didn't meet him. I feel quite educated now. I also feel a bit hungry thinking of chops and trifle.

On the second day, we reached Spain. We passed through Barkalona. It wasn't quite what I expected. I didn't hear any dogs barking. I believe Barkalona is in Catalonia. Very disappointing! No cats about at all! Maybe they were hiding from me...

I was quite exhausted when I arrived. I had a quick look around. The apartment seemed very nice and then I just conked out fast asleep. The floors were nice and cool.

The next day it was very hot and people were dancing outside. I think there was some sort of a nightclub there and they were practicing. Diane said it was flamenco dancing. What on earth was that all about?

I soon found out when I went out on those hot pavements! I was clicking my heels and throwing myself about like the best of them. It was horrendous! Oh my poor feet!

After that, I just refused to go out anymore in the afternoons.

Mom came over for a week or so and when she was there, she took me out early in the morning when it was cool.

She didn't like the heat much either, so that was okay. No more flamenco dancing for me, thank goodness!

I was a bit concerned about the Spanish cuisine.

Well, I know Mom's husband Ken was never too fussy, or so I heard, but Diane, Paul, and Elizabeth enjoyed it. I didn't like the food much either, but I had a good meal one night. I ate some designer sandals, pure leather! They belonged to a friend of Di's. She was very nice but not after I ate her sandals. What was all the fuss about? She could've bought another pair from Pribark.

I didn't like the Spanish water. I got a bit de-higrated, I think that's the right word. I was very thirsty. Mom mixed the water with a little drop of milk, which made it okay.

Wow, it was hot in Spain. I had no energy at all.

They thought I was being very good, but I was sick with exhaustion. Paula always says that when she's had a hard day at school. I didn't have the energy to jump up on anyone.

The Spanish dogs didn't like me at all.

I think it was because I couldn't bark in Spanish. A lot of them hadn't ever seen a chocolate Labrador. They were quite scared. I liked that. It made me feel important.

We go up to see Kev sometimes in Yorkshire and it is lovely up there. It's like a holiday place. I always think I'm on my holidays when I go. I usually take Col and Mom with me, I can't drive, you see. I've never learned. I'm sure I could if I was taught.

We go walking up there and there's a sort of lake, they call it 'the Tarn.' There are ducks and swans there. I wanted to chase them but they chased me. Col got me out before a big swan took my leg off. I won't do that again!

Kev's also got a pond in his garden. Well, you know what happened? I fell in there too. That was not a nice experience! When Col got me out, I was covered in green slimy stuff and the smell was awful, even for me. I had to be washed and dried before I could go into the house again. I didn't like that experience either. Poor me, and that was supposed to be a holiday! I was glad to get home. Do you know what made it worse? They were all laughing, making fun of me, and taking pictures. That was a bit mean, I thought.

Some funny things happened up there with the birds. There were some big trees in the garden and there was a nest right at the top. I think the magpies built it for themselves but a lot of rooks got up there too. There was a great fight. The rooks won and took over the nest.

I laughed to myself. I don't like magpies. They fight every night at Kev's. They all like to sit on the same roof so there is a lot of screaming from them. Why does it have to be that roof? They're all exactly the same! Stupid things!

I must tell you about a lovely holiday I had in Wales with Paula, Steve, and Mom. It was great! We went to this lovely cottage. It was gorgeous and what's more, it was dog friendly, so I could go. There was only one rule I didn't quite like and that was 'No dogs on the furniture, please.' Well, I had a look at the furniture. It looked quite inviting but I thought, *No, I won't jump on.* I stayed on the floor or in my bed, which Mom had taken with us.

What I liked about Wales most was that it was a doggy friendly country. They had bowls of water outside nearly every shop. I was amazed. You don't get that here. I had a little drink out of almost every one of them, just to let them know how much I appreciated it.

One day we went to a lovely place called Round Roost, well, it sounded like that. There was a river there and Paula took me in for a paddle. It was so cool and this time the water tasted nice as well. We all sat by what looked like an enchanted cottage. It was covered in green stuff, every part of it, even the chimney. Mom thought it was gorgeous.

I wasn't so sure, but it was a lovely day and Steve took pictures of us by the river.

Another day, we went to Lanndodo and up the great Orme, which was like a mountain. Steve drove all the way up, and they were all admiring the view. I'm not into views.

I like a bit of grass to do wees on and a bit of shade to sit in when it's hot. That's about it really with scenery!

When we got to the top, there was a tiny chapel and it was called Saint Tudnose. I thought that was a funny name for a Saint. Perhaps he was Welsh? They do have strange names, very different from ours. It was a dog-friendly church, so I went in. Mom said, "Angel, you know when I say I go to church and you can't come? Well, this is church and you are allowed in."

Lovely! I felt special, really special. It was very quiet in there and quite dark but very pleasant, very peaceful and no smells I recognized. Mom said a prayer to Saint Tudno.

Ah, that was his name! I think God must have been there too. I felt different in there somehow. I couldn't quite put my finger, I mean paw on it.

When we got back to the cottage, we had a barbecue in the garden. It was a lovely, big garden. I could almost get lost there but there was no way out. There were cows in the next field. I think that was the reason. I've never met a cow. I don't know whether I'd like them or not. They are a bit big to play with. I didn't get a chance to steal anything at the barbecue unfortunately, so I just went to sleep.

That night we saw something very special. There were deer! They were in the field near the cottage. We had to stay very quiet because they were very timid, but they didn't come very close. I was quiet and hoped I would see them a bit better because they were quite far away, but they must've known we were there and they went back into the forest.

It was all home tomorrow for us. It had been lovely there though, and the weather was great. It was a little bit too hot for Mom but there was plenty of shade for her to sit in, and Paula and Steve were now as brown as berries. They love the sun. It never gets too hot for them.

On the way home, we were going to Llandudno.

Oh, got the place right this time! Steve said there was a restaurant he liked there. I hoped it was dog friendly. We found it and we asked if there was anywhere we could eat with the dog, me! The lady asked, "Is she well-behaved?"

Well, what do YOU think? I was in!

They thought I was wonderful. They made a big fuss over me, gave me water, and petted me. I love Wales, I do! I was as pleased as Punch. I'd like to go and live there. They know how to treat us dogs. They really respect us.

Oh dear! I've just remembered something Mom said the other day. She said I had 'dog breath.'

I'm not sure whether that is good or bad.

I think I will have to ask Stephanie about it.

She will sort it for me. She's Mom's granddaughter and she's a dentist. I would hate to offend anyone.

Mom's gone away for a couple of weeks and I'm staying with Di and Paul. I'm going to be a perfect pest ALL THE TIME, just to teach Mom a lesson for leaving me.

You see, I know they'll do just as I say. It's like taking chocolate from a baby. I just bark LOUD, about midnight every night, and Di comes down pronto and gets on the settee with me. It's great! She falls for it every time! She's a soft touch.

I really don't like being on my own much. I like people around me all the time. She spoils me rotten. Treats and bones all the time! Di tries to 'get on my good side' but I still keep her on her toes at night.

SASKIA

One day I was just minding my own business, sitting down, waiting to go out, and Di came. Well, what a surprise! She had a little puppy with her.

She introduced her to me and said her name was Saskia. Oh, that did sound posh. Well, she was posh! She came from Southport. Poor me! I came from the boot of a car! Nobody knew my roots really, only that I came from South Wales.

Well, of course Sassy was different. I called her Sassy. I couldn't say Saskia, too hard anyway. She was cute, I liked her. She was like my baby, really. I've never had a little one to look after and I took her under my wing, well, I should say my paw. She loved me, well, who wouldn't? She licked my face. I liked that, so I started to look after her.

She wasn't house-trained. That was the problem, so I tried my best to show her what to do. She was weeing all over the place at first. She had to go out in the garden about every ten minutes, which was ridiculous. Anyway, I showed her what to do. I did a little wee, then she did a little wee. The trouble was she had no control at all. Diane said it was because she was a puppy. Then I remembered I was like that too. I kept on trying and she eventually got the message.

But one day, well, I'll tell you this, we were all very shocked indeed. You see, in Diane's house, she had a baby gate on the staircase because Saskia couldn't be trusted. Mom didn't have a baby gate and Sassy was very cheeky. She ran very quickly up the stairs right into Mom's bedroom and leaped on the bed. And what do you think she did? You'll never believe it. She wee weed right in the middle of the bed! Mom didn't realize and took her downstairs. Well, I couldn't say anything, could I?

Mom took us in the garden so we played outside. Sassy loved biting all the heads off the flowers. That didn't go down too well with Mom. I never do that. I'm quite good in the garden now. I don't pull the flowers out and I don't dig holes. In fact, I'm really good. I'm trying to teach Saskia to do as I say and do as I do. It's not easy! I can tell you she's got a mind of her own, that one!

Getting back to the wee wee in Mom's bed... Wait until you hear what happened!

Mom went to bed, curled up as usual, stretched her legs down the bed, and couldn't believe it. It was soaking wet in the middle! She couldn't understand what had happened. She thought there must be a leak in the roof. She put the lights on, looked up at the ceiling, nothing! She couldn't think straight. She was tired and it was late, so she got out of that bed and went into another bed in another room.

In the morning, she got up and went into her own bedroom and had another look at the bed. The duvet was wet just in the middle and it had gone right through to the mattress.

She thought again and then it dawned on her. Saskia, that's who it was! I cringed, glad it wasn't me. I had never done anything like that in my whole life, never. What a naughty girl!

Mom got on the phone with Diane and told her, and you'll never believe what she said. She said, "Are you sure it wasn't Angel? I can't believe Saskia could do that!"

She did though! I had a little sly smile to myself.

Mom had to throw that duvet away. She said she didn't fancy it anymore. Sassy never got upstairs again. Mom barricaded the stairs and shut all the bedroom doors when she came.

Sassy is growing up really quickly and she is as big as me now. She looks amazing but apparently she has some nasty liver disease so she has a special diet and she can't have any treats. It's a shame for her but okay for me.

I eat her share too. Everybody heaps care and affection on her.

I must say she is lovely but when things get too much, I push her out of the way so I can get petted too. Sometimes I feel like saying, 'what about me, I'm here too, does anybody realize?' Hello, I've got feelings too, you know! Do you know some dogs would do anything to be noticed?

Our friend You Know Who goes for a walk with Diane and me, and when anybody passes, she lies down on her back, kicks her legs in the air, and waits for someone to stroke her. Sure enough, they do. I just walk on regardless.

I couldn't be bothered with that lark. Or she sits and waits until they come near, and then she just looks at them, waiting for them to notice her. She thinks she's great, and I love her to bits. She's also a very good swimmer.

I don't know whether I can swim. I am a bit scared with having a bad leg but I might try if Sassy is with me. I know she'd help me if I got into 'difficulties.'

When she was two, she had a party, if you please. It was a beautiful day and we were all in Diane and Paul's garden.

Elizabeth had bought Sassy a party frock. I ask you, would you credit it? I would have just torn it to shreds if it had been put on me, but she loved it and kept it on all day. I thought she looked ridiculous. Perhaps I was a little bit jealous. We all had a lovely time and lots of goodies. I had Sassy's share too.

OZZY

I must tell you this, I don't like cats. I don't know why I don't like them. I've never really met one face-to-face but I just don't like the look of them. Val, Mom's friend, has got two. Do you know what they do just to annoy me? One sits in the front window, behind the glass, of course, so I can't get him. The other one sometimes sits in the front path, when she knows I'm in the porch and I can't get to her either!

They really get on my nerves.

Cousin Jan has got a cat called Ozzy and he thinks he owns the staircase. Nobody can go up when he's there. Even Jan's grandchildren are too frightened to go upstairs when Ozzy's there. The same can be said of Cousin Sue's dog, Abbie.

Mom didn't know this and she bent over to say hello to Ozzy, and he gave Mom a nasty scratch. Her finger was bleeding.

I don't really think I would like to meet Ozzy. I think he'd probably have a go at my face. I won't take a chance, I think. Mom said he's a lovely cat. I don't think any cats are lovely. They'd all better keep away from me.

Auntie Kath, Mom's sister, is a real cat person. She once had six cats but she didn't want her neighbors to know. She let three cats out at a time and, as they were quite similar, they never knew the difference.

She just has one cat now. He's like the Invisible Man. I've never seen sight nor 'tail' of him. Kath locks him away in the bedroom when she knows I'm coming, I don't know why. I know he's somewhere, as his food is always there.

I lick the dishes. Nice, but not as nice as my food.

Auntie Kath likes me. We go in the car when we go to see her and she lives near the beach. It's really great on the beach. Our Col takes me down and I paddle in the water. It's funny water though. I tried to drink it but it didn't taste nice at all.

The beach is lovely and soft to walk on and you can dig big holes and nobody tells you off. There are some big statues there of giants but they've got no clothes on. They look like sea monsters because they're covered with some horrible green stuff. I like the giants though. They look quite friendly. I think someone should clean them up a bit.

Mom usually takes a nice lunch to Auntie Kath's and Claire comes. Claire is her daughter. Kath loves a bit of company. Sometimes Col and Mom bring fish and chips in or sausage and chips, and of course I get a few too.

We've got other relations that come too. There's Mavis and Ken and our Doreen. They are Mom's in-laws. Doreen is not too well. She has dementia. She loves me, of course. She slips me goodies under the table where no one can see. Mom says, "Please don't feed her, Doreen, she's very greedy."

Me...greedy? I know they're talking about me. I just like food, any sort, any time. It's lovely! Why is that being greedy anyway? Doreen takes no notice and just keeps slipping me the food. Good old Doreen! I always make a big fuss over her. It pays off!

Yippee! I've just heard that Auntie Mavis, Uncle Ken, and Auntie Doreen are coming this afternoon for a cup of tea. Well, you know what that means? I'll be sitting by Doreen and she'll be slipping me goodies under the table and good old Mom won't know anything about it. She'll be too busy talking to Mavis to notice, I hope. I think I heard Mom inviting Doris too. She might drop a few crumbs, Mom certainly will.

I think it's coming up to my dinnertime now so I'll put a sad face on and sit by Mom. It worked! I got my dinner a bit early today, so that was okay.

It was a bit disappointing when the aunties and Doris came. Mom had everything set out in the dining area but they wanted to sit in the garden, didn't they, because it was a nice day and nobody wanted any cake.

I was sitting by Doreen as usual and smiling, as I know she loves me. I was waiting for the goodies. She just managed to slip me one, then Mom saw and said, "Oh no, 'she' (that's me) can't have currants." I was just going to enjoy some, but that was that. I got nothing!

FOXY LADY

I disgraced myself yet again when I was out with Mom the other day. She doesn't take me out very often now because of her legs. She's frightened of me pulling her over.

I have done that a couple of times, not on purpose, of course.

We were having a lovely walk and she let me take the lead. She said, "Don't eat any rubbish because I've got something nice in my pocket!" So I thought, *GREAT!*

I started sniffing around as usual and, oh boy, oh boy, fox poo! I just love the smell of it. I like to roll in it and so I did!

Well, Mom was really furious. *I don't smell too bad,* I thought. I like the smell. It's very different.

When we got home, she poured tomato ketchup all over me. I didn't even get the chance to lick it off! She started rubbing it in, and then washed it all off. So, now I smell like tomato soup! I don't think it's worth doing that again.

We have a few foxes around where I live but I've never seen them. I think they come out at night and go into people's gardens looking for food. I think they live on the railway embankment. It's now been made into a country walk and it's nice up there, especially in the summer.

I really like Posh Park the best. Diane takes Sassy and me up there a lot. We have such fun and we don't get into mischief.

I haven't seen Sassy for ages and ages. I just don't know where she is. I hope she's alright. She used to come on video calls, when Diane was talking to Mom from Spain, until recently.

When Diane and Paul came back, Sassy didn't come with them and they said she was on her holidays. I miss her. I hope she comes home soon.

Paula came down today and I took them up to Diane's house. Well, Paula drove the car, but I directed them from the backseat. I always like going to Diane's because I like to play with Sassy, but she wasn't there. I looked everywhere and went out in the garden but I couldn't find her. I cried. I felt sad.

Elizabeth made a big fuss over me. She has a bad leg. She tripped over and broke a bone. She's got a big, thick plaster on it right up to her knee. All you can see are her toes. I gave them a big lick. She liked that. She said it tickled.

Di rang from Spain while we were there and spoke to me. I barked back at her. I hoped Sassy would hear me and answer me but she didn't. I'm getting more and more worried about her. Diane and Paul are coming home next week by car. If Sassy isn't with them, I just don't know what I'll do.

Elizabeth is not feeling very well at the moment. Mom and Paula made her some food and she felt a bit better. She was going to have a little sleep, so we left her on the settee. I hope her leg gets better soon.

I am not feeling myself at the moment. I've had a very upset stomach. I made an awful mess in the kitchen the other day.

Do you know Mom never shouted at me? She just said, "Poor Angel." I was mortified! But she just cleaned it all up and washed the floor. I felt ill all day and went to bed. I don't feel well yet. I'm still a bit queasy but I had a bit of toast this morning and a few biscuits, so I think I'm on the mend.

I may have to go to the vet's just for a check-up. We go to a nice vet now. The trouble is it's always a bit crowded in there. It's not the dogs that take up the room, it's the people, but I suppose they have to come with us.

When it's my turn, the nurse comes out of the room and calls 'Angel Cunningham.' I get up and trot over to her door. Everyone looks at each other and some say, "What an intelligent dog, she knows her name!" Of course I know my name, I'm not daft.

I just toss my head and walk in. I like it there.

They just check me over and let me leave. Nothing to it! Some of the pooches have to be dragged in, kicking and screaming. Some of them even do a wee on the floor with fright. I've never seen such behavior. I never did anything like that...*or did I?*

FRIENDS FOREVER

Do you know today I just can't stop thinking about Saskia? I've just got a terrible feeling I won't see her ever again. I feel so sad. I've tried asking Mom and Col about her. I brought all her toys in and spread them around me and just looked at Mom. She said, "Angel's never done that before!" Mom looked so sad. I thought, *Why are Sassy's toys here? What am I doing with them?* She doesn't usually let me play with them. I always let her play with mine though.

We had such lovely times together. We were always playing. I tried to keep up with her as best I could. Sometimes, I got really tired but I never went to sleep until she'd gone home.

I didn't really want her to know how tired I was. She never got tired!

I've seen so little of her since the party and I really miss her. *Am I ever going to see her or play with her again?*

I had a dream the other night and I saw Sassy. She was happily playing with Saint Danny, Beau, and Buster. Danny could fly and they were all trying to learn. They were all falling down on a lovely sandy beach. The sun was shining very brightly and there were cats there too but no one was fighting! Maybe I like cats after all. I can't wait to go visit, but only if I can come back to my family.

I do know for certain that I will never forget my wonderful times with my very best friend Saskia. There will never be anyone like her again. I know we will see each other someday, maybe not here but somewhere. I think there is a place called Paradise. Maybe we can all go there. It sounds very grand and we will all be friends together, forever.